Blindside

BY ALEX FRANCIS
ILLUSTRATED BY ALAN BROWN

Walkthrough

Read this first - or turn the page to go straight to the story!

The Characters

Dan

Dan wants to be a doctor. He also loves to play rugby. Can he do both?

Dan's parents

Dan's parents are strict because they want him to be a doctor. They want what's best for Dan.

Matt

Matt is Dan's best friend. He plays rugby and helps Dan join the team.

Key Facts

Scrum

A scrum happens at the beginning of a rugby match. Each player tries to get the ball.

It's important for rugby teams to get together and practise for matches.

Practise

Story Background

Dan wants to be a doctor. His parents want him to study, but he really loves to play rugby.

How can he show them he can do both?

So Dan goes to practice. He has great fun.

Dan runs to the goal line with the ball.

No one can catch him.

The crowd cheers as he drops the ball on the line.

Extra Time...

Answer the questions below. Each correct answer gains you points. Are you a Trainee or a Manager?

1 *Multiple Choice:*
What must Dan do to be a doctor?
a) Play rugby
b) Study lots
c) Go to the library

1pt

2 *Multiple Choice:*
How does Dan go to rugby practice?
a) He asks his parents
b) He doesn't go
c) He sneaks out

1pt

3 Why are Dan's parents worried?

2pts

4 *Fill in the sentence:*
Dan runs to the goal line with the _____.

3pts

6 Multiple Choice: **1pt**
In the end, what do Dan's parents become?
a) His biggest fans
b) Very angry
c) His worst nightmare

Answers on the next page. Every correct answer earns points (pts) Which level are you?

Level:
0 - 1pts = Trainee
2 - 4pts = Substitute
5 - 7pts = Flanker
8 - 9pts = Head Coach
10pts = Manager

Extra Time Answers

1=(b), 2=(c), 3=They think he is being bullied, 4=bal
5=Dan's parents have spotted him at a rugby
match, 6=(a)

Explore...

Think about the following:

- How did Dan feel when he couldn't play rugby?

- Why do you think Dan's parents wanted to stop him playing rugby?

- Do you think Dan's parents were relieved when they found out Dan wasn't being bullied?

Other Titles

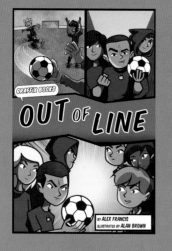